Career Cutouts

Clever and Creative Activities for Kids to "Picture" Themselves in 75 Different Careers

Grades K–3

GREAT FOR:

- bulletin boards
- back-to-school displays
- thematic units

- creative writing
- storytelling
- self-esteem

- unique gifts
- mobiles
- puppets

Written by Phyllis Amerikaner • Illustrated by Bev Armstrong

The Learning Works

Created by
  Phyllis Amerikaner
Illustrated by
  Bev Armstrong
Cover outfit designs by
  Rae Aronoff
Typography by
  Clark Editorial & Design
School photographs by
  Redeye Photography, Santa Barbara, CA

Dedication and Acknowledgments

Special thanks to Leland Graham, to the terrific teachers at Montecito Union—Vicki Harbison and her first grade class, Sue Hillway, and Candy Dunn—to Linda Schwartz, and especially to Steven, David, and Kate.

Copyright © 1997
The Learning Works, Inc.
P.O. Box 6187
Santa Barbara, California 93160
ISBN: 0-88160-294-9

Table of Contents

Table of Contents
continued

Introduction

Career Cutouts can be used in a variety of ways—for bulletin boards, creative writing, art projects, gifts, and so much more. Your students can "try on" 75 different occupations by adding their photos to the cutouts. All you need are photographs, scissors, glue, and crayons or markers. With these readily accessible materials, you will be ready to begin one of the most creative and exciting activities of the school year!

Convenient Features of *Career Cutouts*

- **Two cutouts for each occupation.** Where there is a gender difference in dress, the female figure is pictured on the left of each page, and the male figure is on the right.

- **Short descriptions for each occupation.** Each page includes a simple job description which can be read by the child or teacher, depending on students' abilities. Most descriptions emphasize basic skills—such as math or writing—that are necessary to do the job.

- **Generic cutouts and cutouts of kids in a wheelchair and leg braces.** If students want to choose a career that is not featured in the book, or if you have students who use wheelchairs or leg braces, there are cutouts to accommodate these needs.

- **Reproducible masters for classroom activities.** There are ready-to-use activities on pages 88–91 to expand the uses of the cutouts.

- **Fascinating facts.** Fascinating facts about individual careers appear on pages 92–96. These facts are ideal for classroom discussions.

 ## How to Use *Career Cutouts*

Photos. Have students bring a photo of themselves to class (see page 10 for a sample letter home). Many subwallet-sized school photos will be the right size. If you take the photos yourself, be sure to get a full-face shot. The photos should have a head height of approximately $1^{1}/_{4}$ inches. (Hint: You might want to keep copies of the photos so you will be able to do another *Career Cutouts* activity later in the year. Remember that copyrighted photos should not be copied.) Photos from instant-developing cameras are not recommended, since these photos are not meant to be cut. Check the film box for warnings.

Copying. The cutouts are reproducible for individual classroom use, so they can be enlarged or reduced to suit your needs or to fit the photographs. Copying the cutouts onto heavier-weight paper will help to keep them from curling when they are colored, especially if you are using water-based markers.

Coloring. Have students color the cutouts before they add their photographs. Crayons and pencils in multicultural colors work especially well for skin tones. Encourage students to add details, such as plaids, stripes, and patterns, to the clothing.

Pasting. Use glue or glue sticks to mount the photographs on the colored cutouts.

Laminating. The finished cutouts can be laminated for extra strength.

Creative Project Ideas

Community Helper/Career Units

- **Make "When I Grow Up" pictures.** Mount the finished cutouts on a piece of drawing paper. Have the children draw the surrounding scene.

- **Shrink the cutouts to use as name tags for field trips.**

- **Provide a follow-up activity after a field trip.** After a visit to the public library, for example, use the librarian or author cutouts to write or tell about the field trip.

- **Use the cutouts for bulletin boards or classroom door displays.**

- **Make mobiles.** Provide cutouts in selected categories (transportation, safety, sports, etc.). Let students decide which category their occupation belongs to. Make a mobile for each category.

- **Use the cutouts to make thank you notes for guest speakers.**

- **Create a community as a cooperative learning project.** Use boxes and other reusable materials to design a model community. Add the cutouts to the scene.

- **Make an oversized map of your neighborhood.** Have the students add the appropriate cutout to the site of your local post office, police station, grocery store, etc.

- **Use the cutouts as illustrations for research reports and creative writing projects.**

- **Shrink the cutouts for dioramas.**

Across the Curriculum

Language Arts

- **Become a character in a book.** For example, if you read *Make Way for Ducklings*, let each child make a police officer cutout. Have the students write a story as if they were the police officer who helps the ducklings cross the busy street, or use the reporter cutout and have the students write a newspaper account of the ducklings' adventures.

- **Make a reading game.** Draw a grid on a large piece of paper or poster board. Write a different occupation in the center of each square. Let the children take turns matching their cutouts to the words on the grid.

- **Perform a stick-puppet play or skit.** Tape or glue a wooden stick to the back of each laminated cutout to make stick puppets.

- **Create characters for a story.** Let the children select a cutout to be the main character in a story they write. Use the cutout to illustrate the cover of the book.

- **Reinforce library skills.** Have students list library rules or the titles of books they read during the year. Use the librarian cutout as illustration.

Across the Curriculum
(continued)

Science

- **Supplement science units.** Here are some suggestions:

<u>When you study:</u>   <u>Use this cutout:</u>
dinosaurs   paleontologist
ocean life   marine biologist
plants   gardener or botanist
weather   meteorologist
stars and planets   astronomer or astronaut
the environment   recycling worker

If one can of corn costs 82¢, how much do three cans of corn cost?

Math

- **Write simple word problems using the cutouts as illustrations.**

- **Make a classifying and sorting game.** Draw a chart on the blackboard with several columns. Head each column with a category: safety, the arts, sports, and science, for example. Have students write their names in the column that best describes the category to which their occupation belongs.

Art

- **Make individual or group murals.**

- **Add pizzazz!** Decorate the cutouts with wrapping paper, aluminum foil, fabric scraps, ribbon, and other odds and ends.

- **Make stick puppets using the cutouts.**

The Tigers Tackle the Timber Wolves

Physical Education

- **Write sports stories.** Use the "Be a Sport" cutouts for illustrations.

- **Make class teams.** Choose a sports cutout. Divide the class into teams. Let each team design a logo and select team colors. Have each team list the skills needed to play the selected sport.

Year-Round Uses

Fall

- **Make a display for the first day of school.** Enlarge the teacher cutout and add your photograph to make a personalized door display.

- **Use the cutouts to help children learn each other's names.** Seat your class in a semicircle on the rug. Hold up a finished cutout and have someone say who it is.

- **Make bulletin board for Back-to-School Night**, or place a finished cutout on each child's desk to help parents find their child's seat.

- **Make a career costume parade on your bulletin board.** This is a great October activity to let the kids "dress up" in a cutout of their choice.

- **Increase election awareness.** In election years, have students make a mayor, president, or judge cutout and let the students write about what it would be like to hold that office.

Winter

- **Make original Christmas, Hanukkah, or Kwanzaa gifts.** Have your students make a cutout for a parent or other special person. After they sign the back of the cutout, laminate it to create a personalized bookmark, gift tag, or ornament.

- **Provide a Martin Luther King Day activity.** Make a bulletin board display of students' career choices. Entitle it "I Have a Dream . . . and Anything is Possible for Me!" You could also have students select cutouts to show their dream for the world—the president for world peace or the police officer for safe streets, for example.

- **Make a Valentine's Day mobile.** Have students choose a cutout of a person in a "caregiving" occupation—nurse, veterinarian, teacher, parent, etc.—and make a mobile out of the cutouts. Add construction paper hearts hanging at various lengths.

- **Make a Presidents' Day display.** Give a president cutout to each of your students and let them draw or write what they would do if they were president.

Year-Round Uses

Spring

- **Make a springtime display.** Use the theme "Spring into Action" and feature the dancer, tennis pro, baseball player, gardener, house painter, and other appropriate cutouts.

- **Make a "Spring Forward Twenty Years" display.** Let the kids write about what they think they will be doing in twenty years.

- **Write year-end thank you cards.** Make cutouts of the people who have been helpful to your students during the school year—parent volunteers, crossing guards, principal, bus driver, etc.—and turn them into thank you cards.

Teacher Tips

What If?

- *a student forgets to bring a photo or you have no photo available?*

  Have the children draw their faces onto the cutouts. They can add hair, glasses, and other details.

- *the photograph is the wrong size?*

  Unless the photo is substantially oversized or undersized, most kids won't mind. If necessary, shrink or enlarge the photo on a copy machine. Kids can color the skin tone and hair to create a color photo effect.

- *a student brings in a photo from an instant-developing camera?*

  Use a photocopy of the photo or let the child draw a face on the cutout.

Share Your Ideas!

Career Cutouts provides opportunities to stimulate your students' creativity and imagination. Once you get started, you will probably think of many other ways to use the cutouts in this book. Please write to us and tell us about your ideas. We will credit you with any ideas we use in future books. We would love to hear from you!

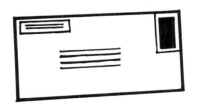

Career Cutouts **Ideas**
The Learning Works
P.O. Box 6187
Santa Barbara, CA 93160

Sample Letter Home

Here is a sample letter you can use to inform parents about your upcoming *Career Cutouts* activities.

Dear Parents,

In a few weeks, our class will be doing a creative classroom project. Because this project uses photographs, I need your help. Please send me a photo of your child in which the head is approximately 1^1/$_4$ inches in height. <u>The photo will be cut, so please don't send a picture that you need to have returned.</u>

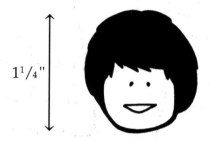

1^1/$_4$"

Subwallet-sized photos from a school photo packet may work, but you might want to measure the head size to be sure. If you send in a personal photo, it should include a full-face shot of your child, not a profile. We ask that you do not send photos from instant-developing cameras, since these photos should not be cut.

I know you will be delighted with the way your child will be "pictured" in this exciting classroom activity. If you are unable to provide a photograph, please let me know. I am available to answer any questions you might have.

Sincerely,

Please turn in your photograph by _____

Fire Fighter

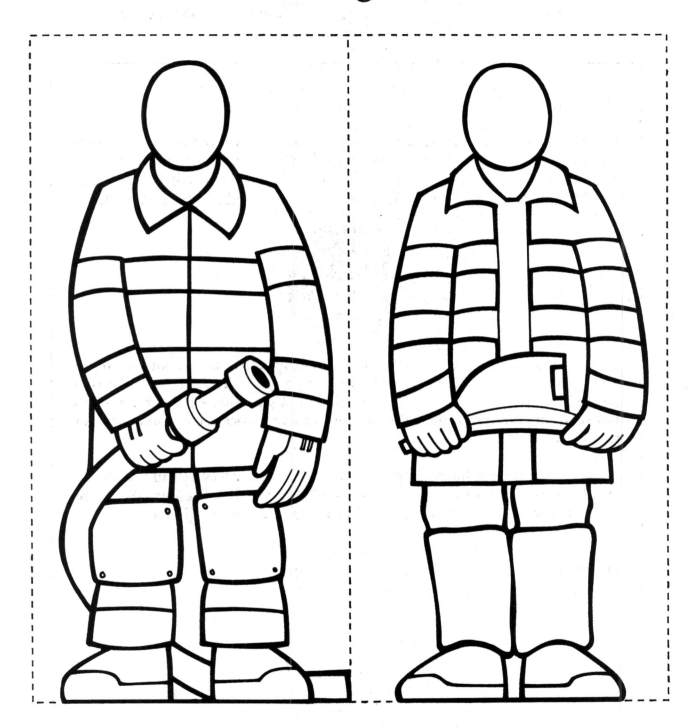

Fire fighters wear special uniforms to protect themselves from heat, smoke, and flames when they fight fires. They also teach children about fire safety.

Paramedic

Paramedics give **emergency** medical care. They help people who **are hurt in** accidents. Paramedics ride in ambulances.

Police Officer

Police officers work hard to stop crime and to keep people safe. They help when there is an emergency such as a car accident or a robbery.

Crossing Guard

Crossing guards stop cars so children can cross the street safely on their way to and from school. They wear bright jackets so drivers can see them.

Day-Care Provider

Day-care providers take care of very young children.
They plan fun things to do, serve snacks, and make
sure the children are safe and happy.

Principal

Principals help schools run smoothly. They work with teachers, students, and parents. They make sure school is a good place for kids to learn.

Teacher

Teachers help children learn about many subjects such as reading, math, and science. They make learning fun and interesting.

Bank Teller

Bank tellers help people put money in and take money out of the bank. They use math every day to count money and make change.

Grocery Clerk

Grocery clerks help people purchase food and other things at the grocery store. They use computer scanners and scales. They use math to make change.

Librarian

Librarians help children find good books to read. They make sure the books are in the correct order on the library shelves.

Mail Carrier

Mail carriers deliver letters and packages to homes and businesses. They make sure all the mail goes to the right addresses.

Real Estate Agent

FOR SALE
CALL
VALLEY REALTY

OPEN HOUSE

Real estate agents help people rent, buy, and sell homes, businesses, and land. They use math to add prices and rents. They use maps in their work.

Recycling Worker

PLASTIC

Recycling workers collect bottles, cans, and papers to be recycled. Workers pick up these things from people's homes or collect them at recycling centers.

Sanitation Worker

Sanitation workers pick up garbage from homes and businesses. They need to be strong to lift heavy trash cans. They drive in or ride on big trucks.

The 911 operators get calls from people when there is an emergency. The 911 operator tells fire fighters, paramedics, or police where to go to help.

Parent

Parents make sure their children are healthy and happy. They show their children lots of love. Being a parent is a very important job.

Reporter

News reporters write for newspapers and magazines.
Most of them use computers to write their stories.
Television reporters tell about the news on TV.

Mechanic

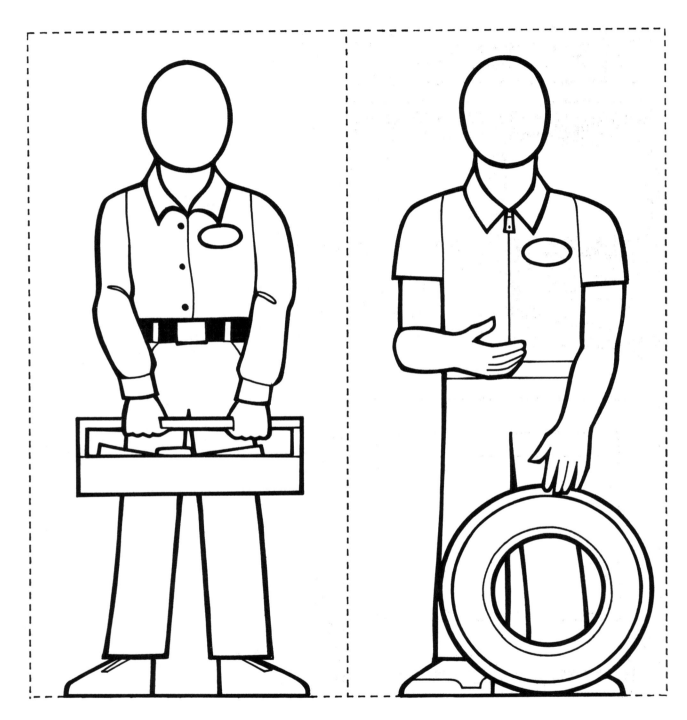

Mechanics fix cars that have problems. Mechanics are good at working with tools. They know a lot about engines.

School Bus Driver

School bus drivers bring children to and from school. They must be very safe drivers. It is an important job to drive busloads of children.

Train Conductor

Train conductors help people on and off the train.
They collect tickets. People ask the conductor for
help if they need it while they are on the train.

Truck Driver

TRUCKING COMPANY

Truck drivers move large loads from place to place. They drive moving vans, big rigs, dump trucks, and delivery trucks. They must be careful drivers.

Air Traffic Controller

Air traffic controllers keep track of planes flying in and out of an airport. They tell the pilots when it is safe to land or take off.

Astronaut

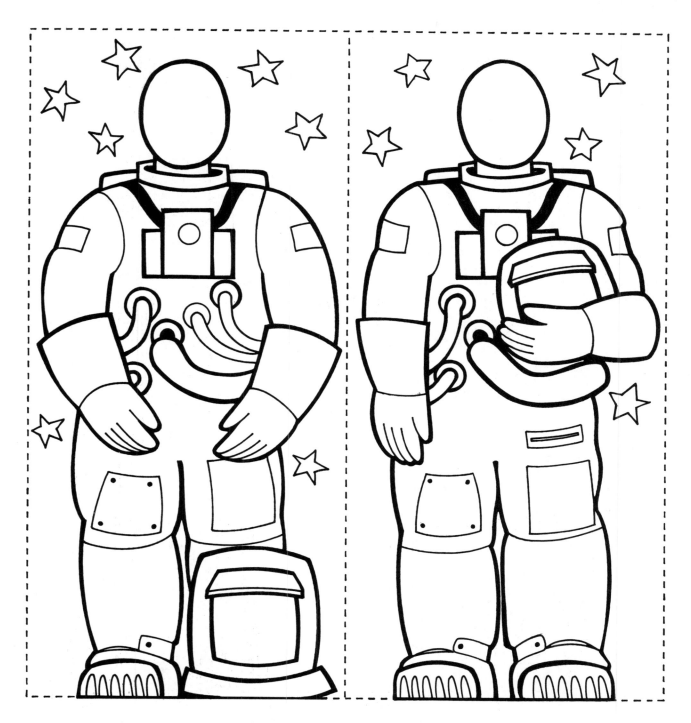

Astronauts fly in spacecraft high above the earth. They help scientists learn more about the stars, the planets, and space travel.

Flight Attendant

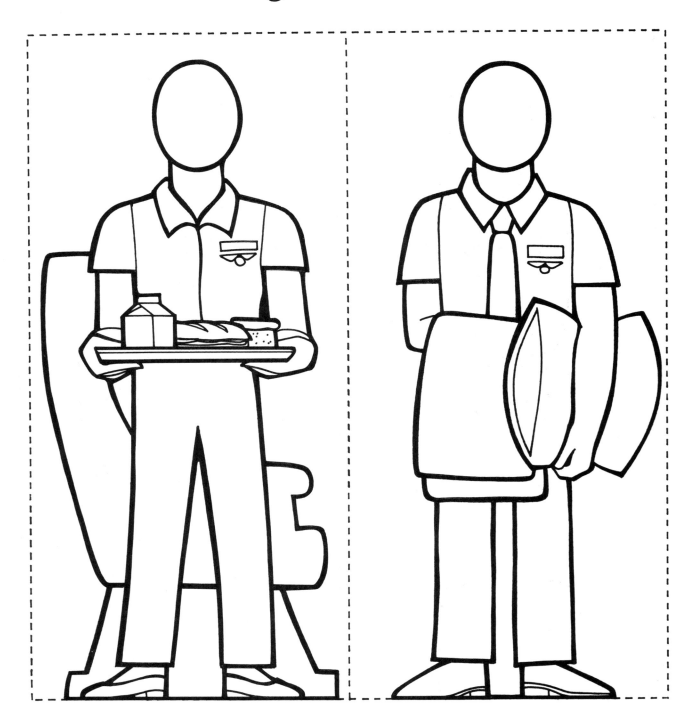

Flight attendants make sure that people on an airplane are safe and comfortable. They explain the safety rules of the plane and serve meals and drinks.

Pilot

Pilots fly airplanes from city to city. Some planes carry people. Others carry cargo. Pilots must be rested and alert so they can fly the plane safely.

Architect

PROPOSED SHOPPING CENTER

_____

ARCHITECT

Architects draw designs called "blueprints" for houses and buildings. Architects measure carefully to make sure the buildings are designed correctly.

Brick Layer

Brick layers build houses and walls by setting bricks side-by-side. They fill the spaces between the bricks with a special kind of cement called "mortar."

Carpenter

Carpenters build things from wood. They make houses, furniture, and cabinets. They must know how to measure carefully and to use tools safely.

House Painter

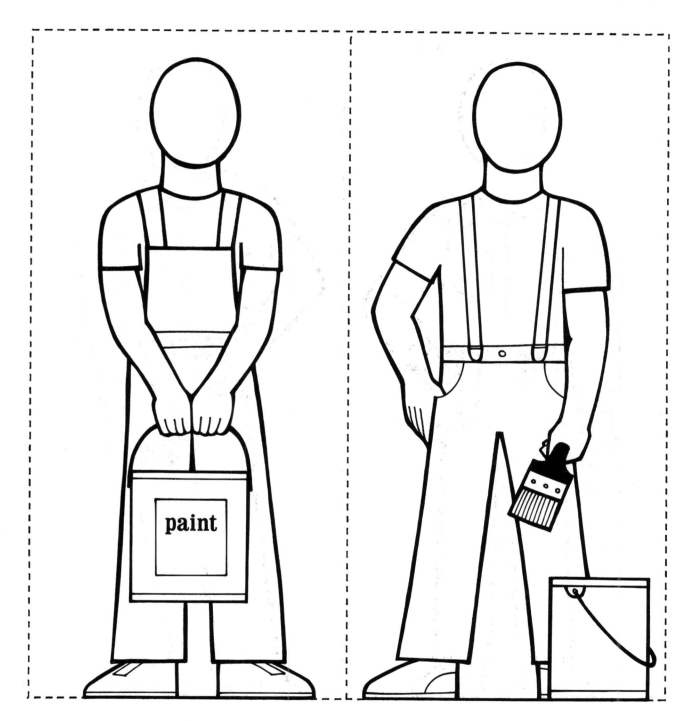

House painters use brushes, rollers, and sprayers.
They stand on ladders to paint high places. Paint
helps to protect a house and make it look nice.

Plumber

Plumbers fix broken pipes and clogged drains. They install sinks, toilets, and bathtubs in homes and offices. They know a lot about water and pipes.

Clothing Designer

Clothing designers draw new ideas for clothes. They know a lot about colors and fabrics. They must be good artists and have good imaginations.

Hairdresser

Hairdressers use scissors, brushes, and curlers to cut and style people's hair. They go to a special school to learn how to make people's hair look good.

Sales Clerk

Sales clerks work in **stores** and help people who buy things. They **must** know **how to** use a cash register. It is their job to be friendly and helpful.

Dentist

Dentists take care of people's teeth and gums. They give tips on how to brush and floss. They look at x-rays of teeth and fill any cavities they find.

Doctor

Doctors help people feel better when they are sick or hurt. They also try to keep people from getting sick. Doctors know a lot about the human body.

Nurse

Nurses help people who are sick. They take temperatures and give medicines. Nurses work in hospitals, doctors' offices, and clinics.

Optometrist

Optometrists give people tests to find out if they
need to wear glasses. They make sure the glasses
look good and fit properly.

Orthodontist

Orthodontists help people have straighter teeth.
They use special wires and bands called "braces" to
slowly move the teeth into place.

Baker

Bakers make bread, rolls, cookies, and cakes. They work late at night or early in the morning to make sure bakeries have fresh baked goods each day.

Chef

Chefs work in restaurant kitchens to prepare meals. They must be able to measure carefully and follow the directions in a recipe.

Farmer

Farmers grow food for people to eat. They know a lot about seeds and plants. Some farmers raise animals such as chickens and cows.

Waiter/Waitress

Waiters and waitresses work in restaurants. They take meal orders and bring people food and drinks. They use math to count change and add up bills.

Camp Counselor

Camp counselors make sure kids at camp have a good time. They plan fun projects and field trips. They lead the campers in songs and games.

Gardener

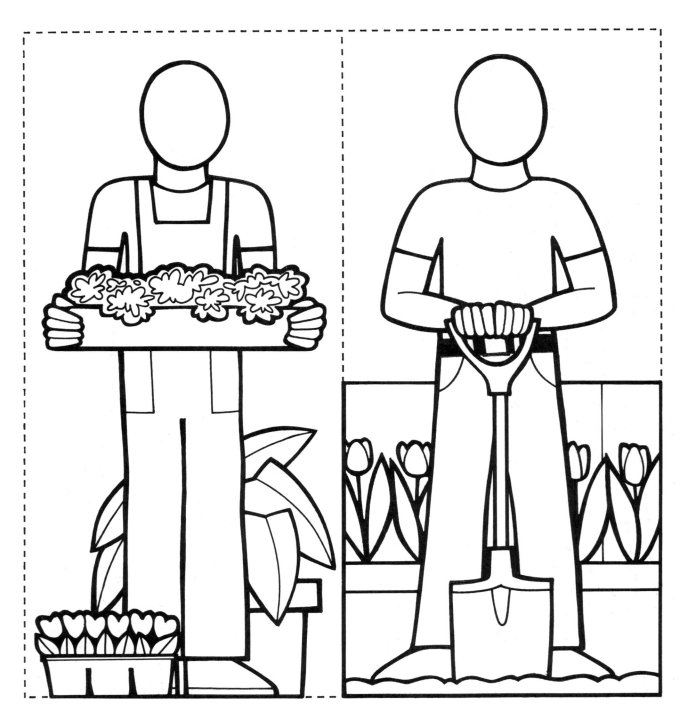

Gardeners take care of flowers, trees, and other plants. They work in garden centers, yards, and parks. They know how to keep plants healthy.

Lifeguard

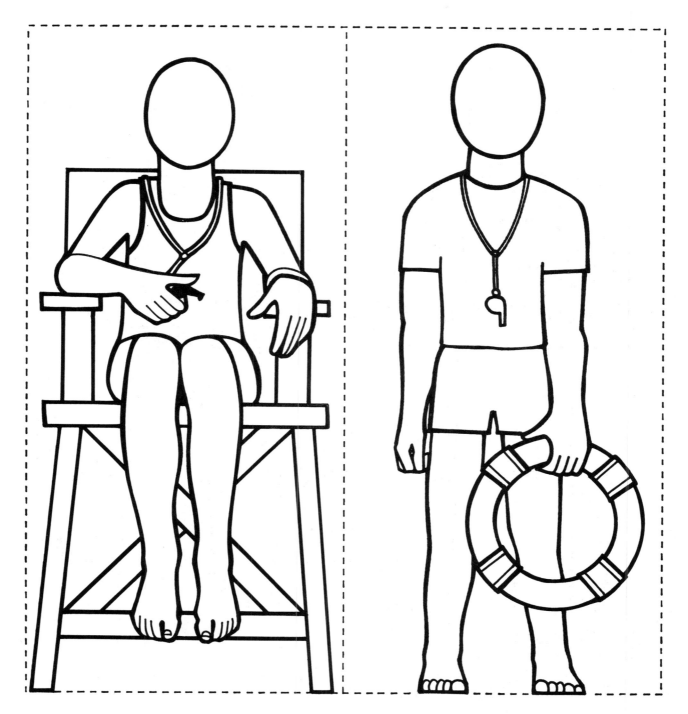

Lifeguards make sure people who are swimming in pools or oceans are safe. Lifeguards must be good swimmers. They know a lot about first aid.

Park Ranger

Park rangers take care of forests and parks. They know a lot about plants and animals. They give tours and information to park visitors.

Actor

Actors work in plays, in the movies, or on television. They are good at pretending. They must memorize lots of lines to play their parts.

Artist

Artists make beautiful things for people to look at.
Some artists sell their work. Some teach drawing and
painting. Artists know a lot about color and design.

Author

BOOK SIGNING TODAY

PRESENTING AUTHOR

_____

Authors write stories and books. Authors are good with words. They must have good imaginations and be able to write well.

Dancer

**Dancers move their bodies to music. Some dancers
study ballet. Others learn jazz, folk, or tap dance.
Dancing is good exercise.**

Musician

Musicians play instruments such as pianos, violins, guitars, and drums. Some play in bands or with orchestras. Some teach music to others.

Photographer

Photographers use cameras to take school, family, or wedding photos. Some photographers sell their photos to newspapers or magazines.

Baseball Player

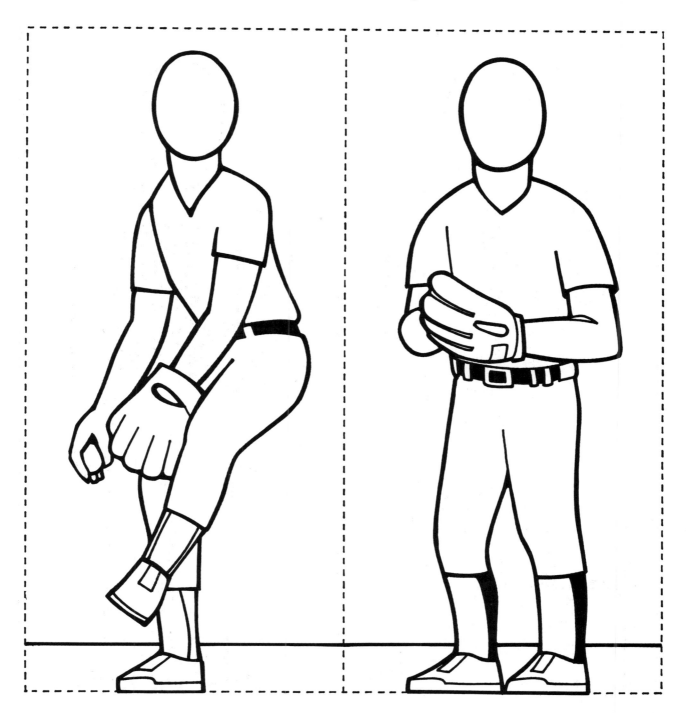

Baseball players are good at throwing, hitting, and catching. They use bats, gloves, and helmets. It takes a lot of teamwork to play baseball.

Basketball Player

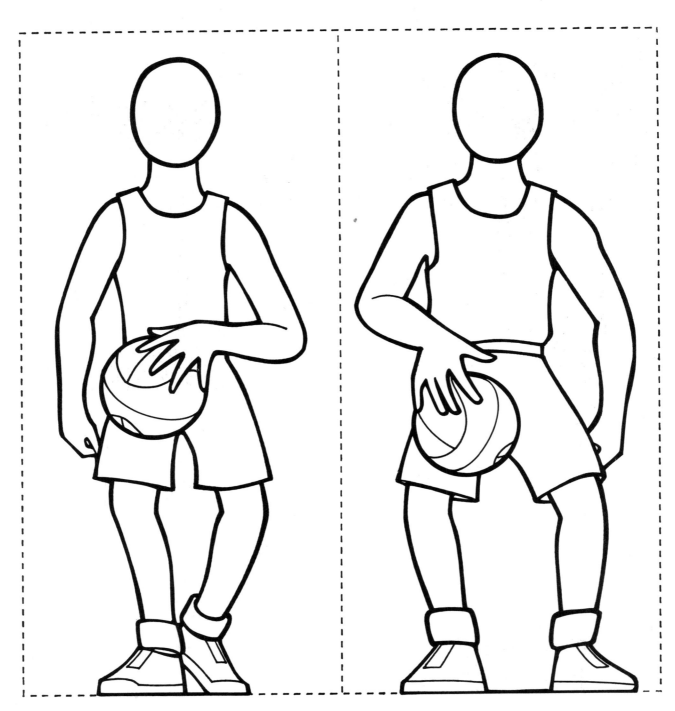

Basketball players practice running, dribbling, and shooting. Basketball players must be in top shape to run up and down the court.

Football Player

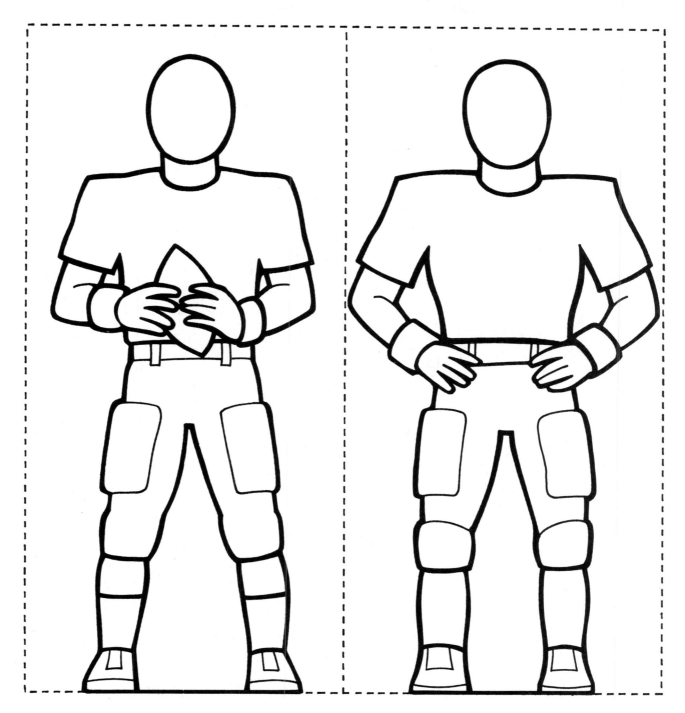

Football players are good runners, tacklers, throwers, and catchers. They wear helmets and pads to protect themselves from getting hurt.

Ice Skater

Ice skaters must be strong and graceful to do their skating routines. Ice skaters work at rinks, perform in shows, or enter skating contests.

Sports Official

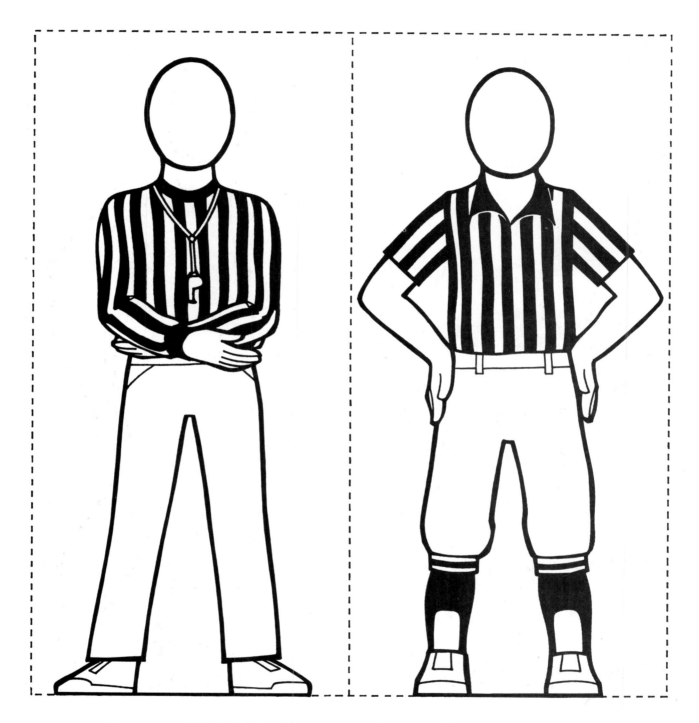

Sports officials make sure players follow the rules during games. Baseball officials are called umpires. Football and basketball officials are called referees.

Tennis Pro

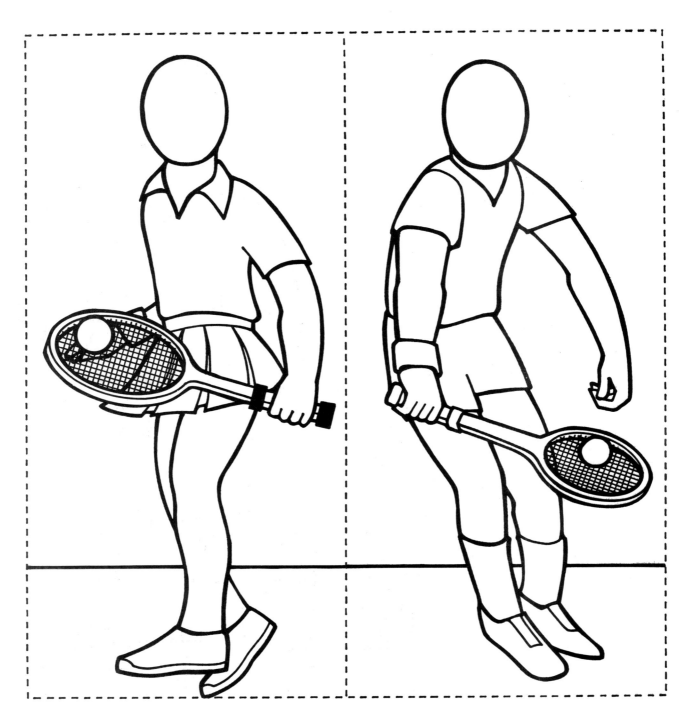

Tennis pros must watch carefully and move quickly
to hit the ball. Some tennis pros play in tournaments.
Others teach people how to play the game.

Horse Trainer

Horse trainers teach horses to carry riders and obey commands. Trainers must know how to work safely around horses.

Pet Groomer

Pet groomers give dogs and cats their baths, trim their fur, and clip their nails. They help pets get rid of fleas. Groomers enjoy being around animals.

Veterinarian

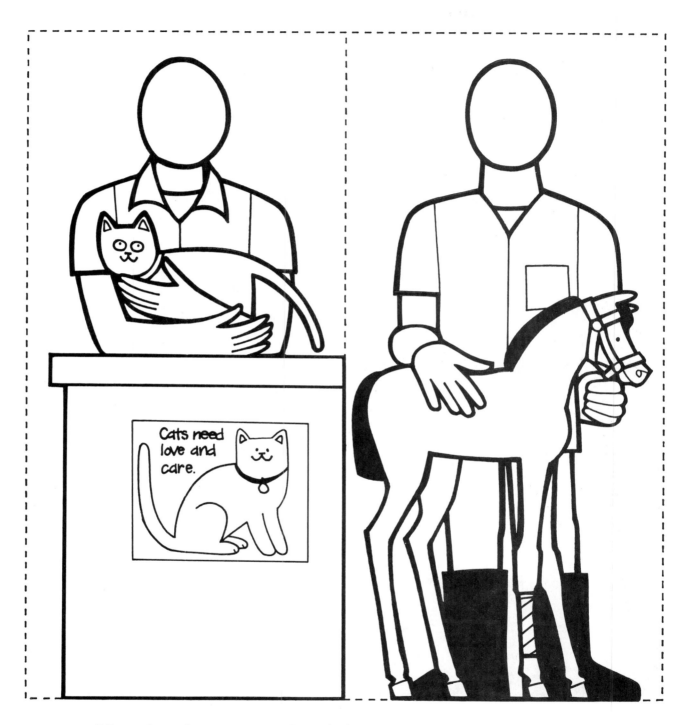

Veterinarians are animal doctors. Some take care of dogs, cats, and other small pets. Others take care of zoo animals or farm animals.

Zoo Keeper

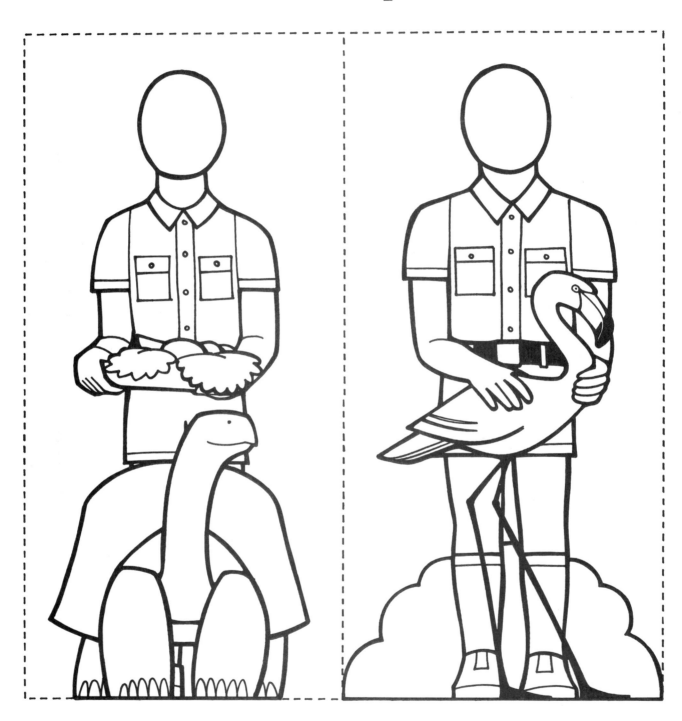

Zoo keepers take care of zoo animals. They feed them, clean their cages, and make sure they are healthy. Zoo keepers enjoy being around animals.

Judge

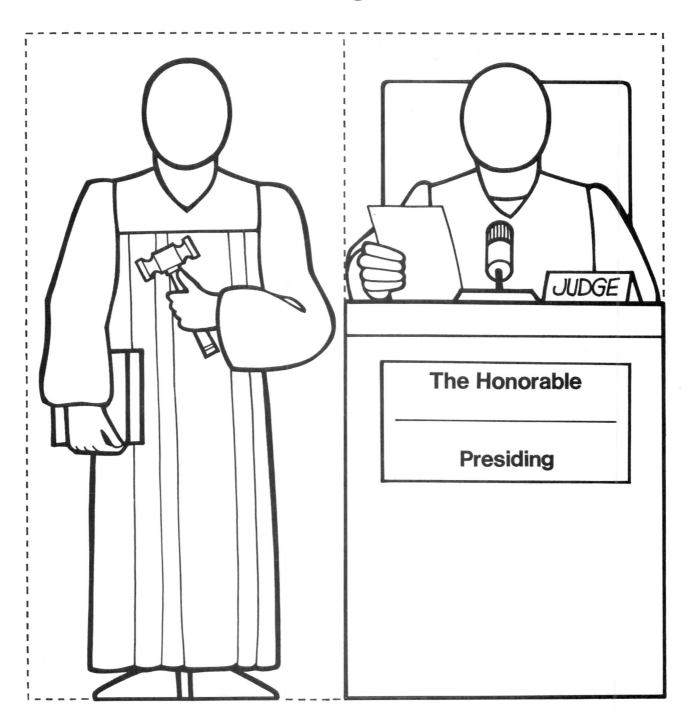

The Honorable

_____

Presiding

JUDGE

Judges keep order in the courtroom. They must know about laws. It is important for judges to be fair when they make their decisions.

Lawyer

Lawyers give advice to people about the law. They work in offices and sometimes go to court. They must be good writers and problem solvers.

Mayor

Mayors are the leaders of towns and cities. They go to meetings, welcome visitors, and help to make their cities safer and cleaner.

President

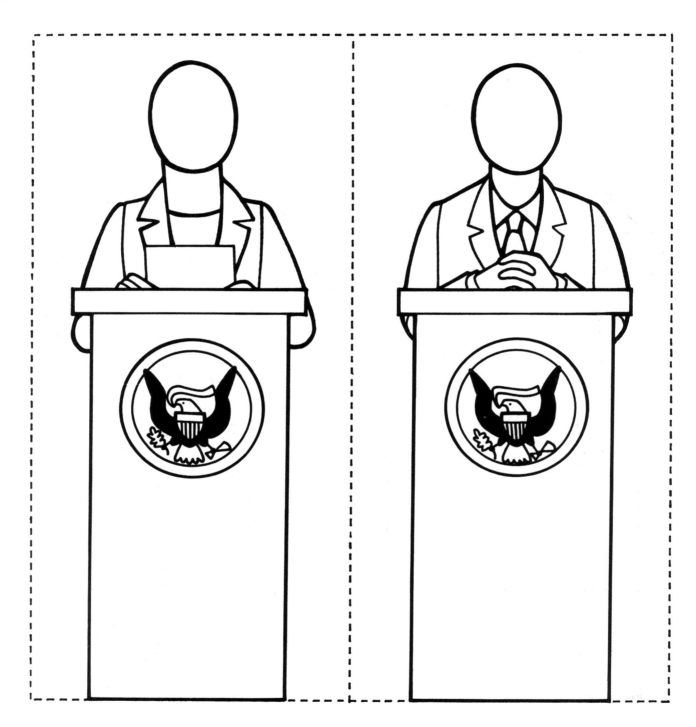

The president is the leader of the United States. The president lives in the White House in Washington, D.C. People vote for a president every four years.

Astronomer

Astronomers study stars and planets. They use big telescopes in their work. Sometimes they get pictures from cameras that are sent into space.

Botanist

Botanists study plants. They find new ways to use plants for food and medicine. They also find ways to protect plants from diseases.

Computer Game Designer

Computer game designers write programs for computers. They must be very creative. Sometimes they make games to help kids with math or reading.

Entomologist

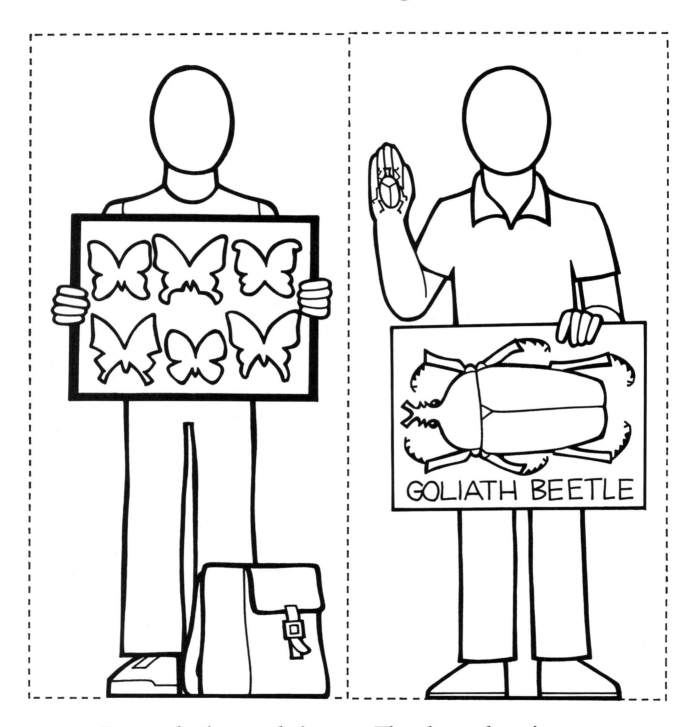

GOLIATH BEETLE

Entomologists study insects. They know how insects grow, eat, and live. They learn how to control harmful insects such as flies and termites.

Geologist

Geologists study rocks and minerals to learn more
about the earth. Sometimes they discover oil, coal,
gold, or diamonds. Some geologists collect rocks.

Marine Biologist

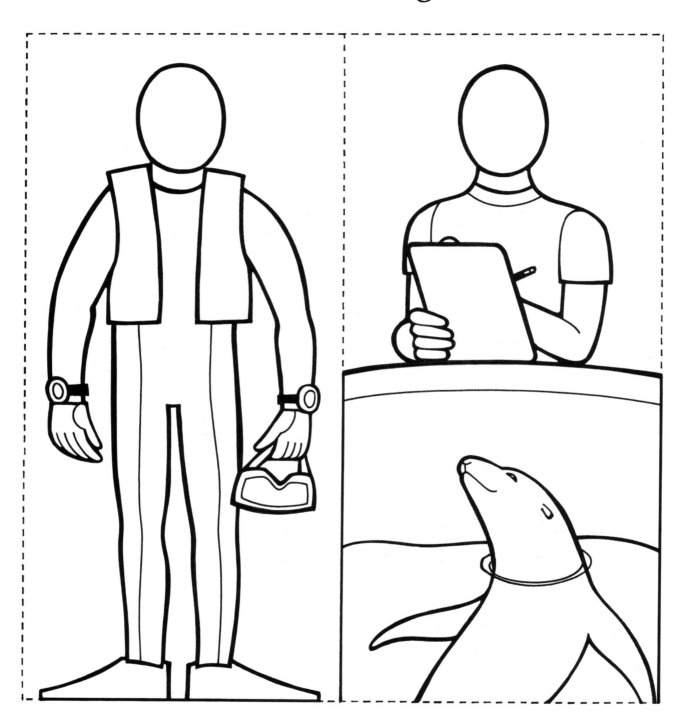

Marine biologists study plant and animal life in the ocean. They try to find ways to keep ocean life safe from pollution.

Meteorologist

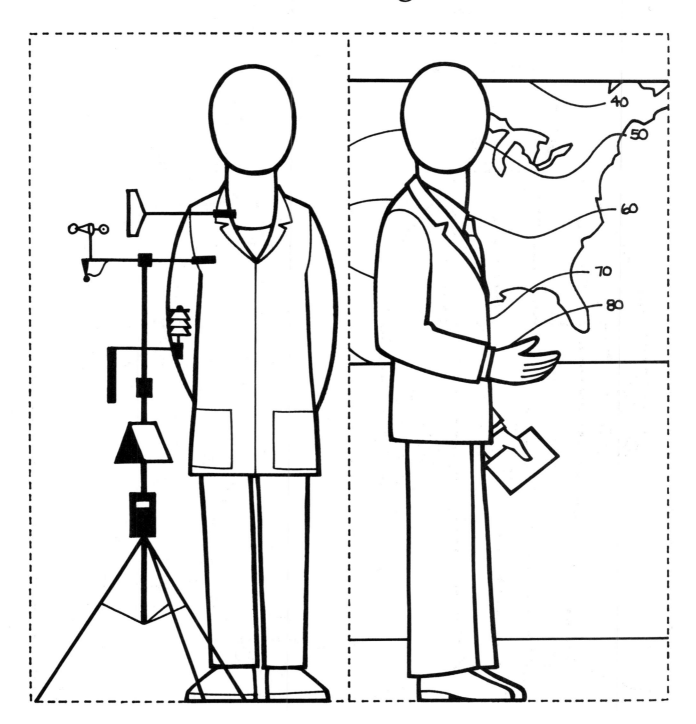

Meteorologists study the weather. They use special equipment to help them tell when there will be rain, snow, storms, or sunshine.

Paleontologist

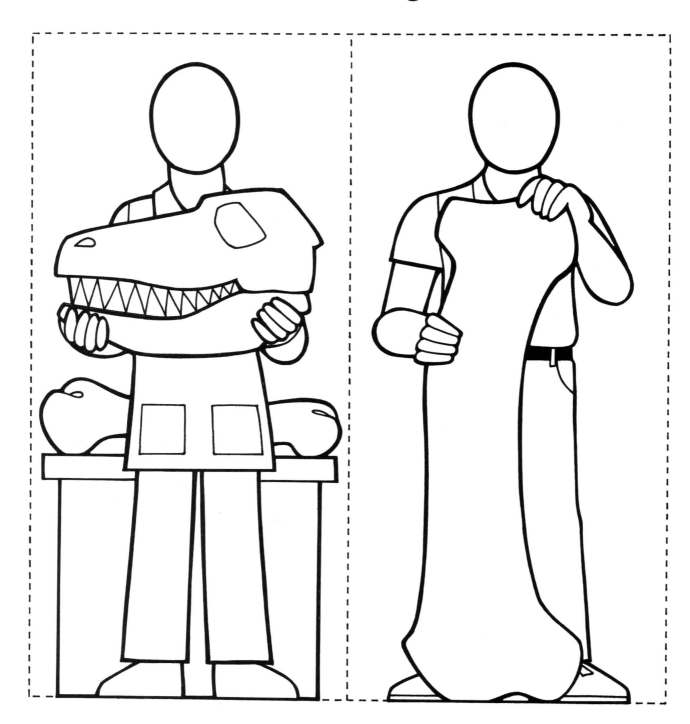

Paleontologists study "fossils," the remains of plants
and animals that lived long ago. Fossils can be found
in rocks, ice, tar, lava, or amber.

Research Scientist

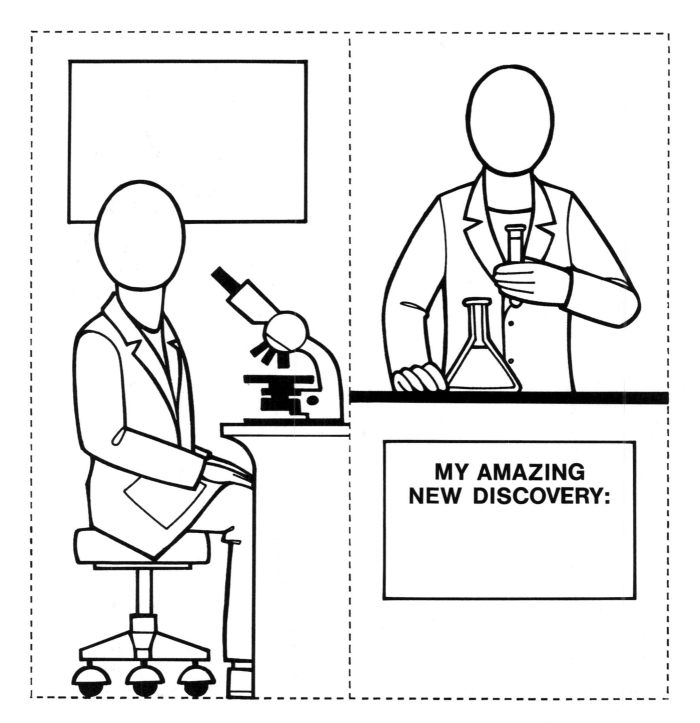

MY AMAZING
NEW DISCOVERY:

Research scientists try to learn more about things
like medicine, space, light, plants, and animals.
Many scientists use microscopes in their work.

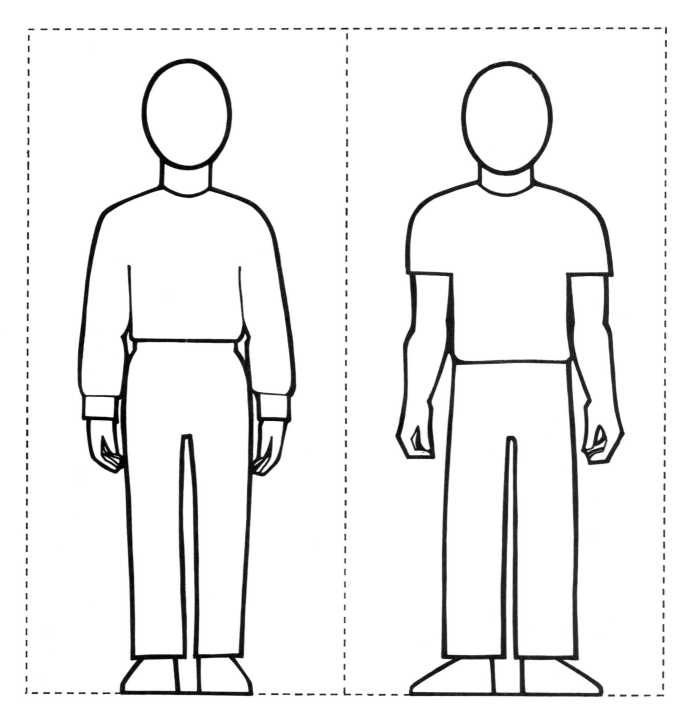

Use these cutouts to design any career you like, such as:

detective	inventor	racecar driver	security guard
film director	magician	secretary	tour guide

Cutouts with
Wheelchair/Leg Braces

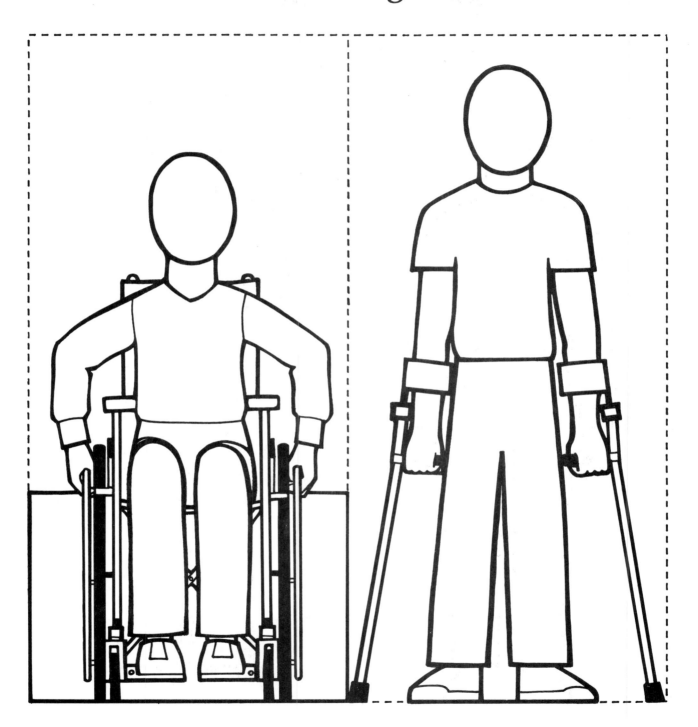

Use these cutouts to show yourself in the job of your
dreams. Add details to the scene to show the things
you would use in your job.

Headline News

Imagine that, while doing your job one day, you did an amazing thing. Maybe you made an important discovery, created a new invention, made a game-winning catch, or even saved someone's life. Write a newspaper story about what you did and how you felt. Draw your picture in the small box below.

AMAZING JOB BY LOCAL HERO!

By _____

Design an Award

People who do their work well sometimes get special awards for things such as:

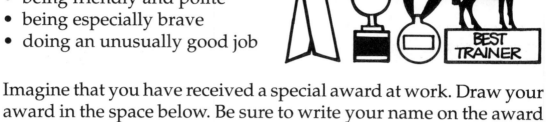

- having great ideas
- being friendly and polite
- being especially brave
- doing an unusually good job

Imagine that you have received a special award at work. Draw your award in the space below. Be sure to write your name on the award and tell why you received it.

What's My Job?

Read the poem at the bottom of the page. Can you guess
what kind of job this person does? Connect the dots to find out!

My job is the best! I've always said.
I paint my smile so true.
My shoes are big, my nose is red
My hair is green and blue.

And when I work, kids laugh at me
Whenever I fall down
I love my job, I shout with glee
For I'm a funny _____!

How I Helped the World

I am proud of myself. Because of the work I have done, the world is a better place in which to live. Here is what I did.

_____

_____

_____

_____

_____

_____

_____

_____

_____

Fascinating Facts

ACTOR Shirley Temple appeared in her first film in 1931 at the age of three. Three years later, she was the star of her own film.

AIR TRAFFIC CONTROLLER The world's busiest airport is O'Hare in Chicago. A plane takes off or lands there on an average of every 37 seconds.

ARCHITECT As a senior at Yale, Maya Lin won a contest to design the Vietnam War Memorial in Washington, D.C. Her design was selected from more than 1,400 entries.

ARTIST Many consider the "Mona Lisa" by Leonardo da Vinci to be the world's most valuable painting. It was once valued at more than $100 million.

ASTRONAUT In July 1969, Neil Armstrong became the first person to walk on the moon. Then-president Richard Nixon called, making the first phone call to the moon!

ASTRONOMER The sun contains more than 99% of the mass of our solar system. The temperature of the sun ranges from 10,000°F on the surface to more than 25,000,000°F in its center.

AUTHOR Georges Perec, a French author, wrote a book called *A Void*, in which no word contained the vowel *e*. The book was then translated into English—without any *e*'s!

BAKER The first chocolate chip cookie was baked at the Toll House Inn near Whitman, MA, around 1930. To make the chips, Ruth Wakefield chopped up a large chocolate bar.

BANK TELLER Other things that have been used as money include wood, stones, shells, deerskin, feathers, skulls, salt, potatoes, dried tea, dogs' teeth, and cattle.

BASEBALL PLAYER The first professional baseball team was the Cincinnati Red Stockings, formed in 1869. The highest-paid player received $1,400 a year. A ticket cost only 10¢.

BASKETBALL PLAYER Basketball was first played in Springfield, MA, in 1891. James Naismith nailed peach baskets to a gym balcony. Players threw a ball into the basket and then had to climb a ladder to get it back.

BOTANIST While some plants seem to grow very slowly, some varieties of bamboo grow up to three feet a day!

BRICK LAYER Bricks, which are made of clay, have been used in the construction of buildings for more than 6,000 years.

CAMP COUNSELOR The first summer camp was organized in Connecticut in 1861. Now there are more than 8,500 camps in the United States.

CARPENTER Nails are measured in units called "pennies," abbreviated as *d*. A one-inch nail, for example, is called a two-penny nail or 2d.

CHEF Fannie Farmer, a graduate of the Boston Cooking School in the 1880s, was the first to write recipes that used precise measurements such as cups and teaspoons.

Fascinating Facts

CLOTHING DESIGNER In the 1800s, women wore crinolines made of linked steel hoops. Their huge skirts often knocked things over or got caught in wagon wheels.

COMPUTER GAME DESIGNER One of the first computer games was "Pong," which was introduced in 1972.

CROSSING GUARD In the late nineteenth century, policemen helped children cross busy streets to get to school. Women weren't hired as crossing guards until World War II.

DANCER The first ballets were expensive, unprofessional events that were performed for royalty. The dancers, who had no special training, wore heavy costumes and high heels.

DAY-CARE PROVIDER Children have played with toys and games for thousands of years. Archeologists have discovered ancient Roman rag dolls and Egyptian spinning tops.

DENTIST
Early toothbrushes were made of hog bristles, horsehair, or badger hair. The nylon bristle toothbrush was not invented until 1938.

DOCTOR America's first female doctor was Elizabeth Blackwell, who received her medical degree in 1849. She opened the world's first hospital to have an all-female staff.

ENTOMOLOGIST The common housefly can see in many directions at once. It has compound eyes, each made up of 3,000 to 6,000 simple eyes.

FARMER The largest pumpkin on record weighed almost 1,000 pounds. The largest jack o' lantern was carved from a pumpkin weighing more than 825 pounds.

FIRE FIGHTER The first fire engines were simple pumps which squirted a bucketful of water at a time.

FLIGHT ATTENDANT The first flight attendants were eight nurses hired in 1930. In addition to helping passengers, they loaded luggage, moved planes in and out of hangars, and refueled tanks.

FOOTBALL PLAYER Players in early football games did not wear pads or helmets. To protect their heads, some players grew long hair.

GARDENER The first botanical garden in the U.S. opened in 1859 in St. Louis, now known as the Missouri Botanical Garden. Many still call it Shaw's Garden in honor of its founder, Henry Shaw.

GEOLOGIST Salt was so valuable in ancient Rome that soldiers were paid in salt. Even today, the expression "not worth his salt" refers to someone who doesn't do a good job.

GROCERY CLERK The Piggly-Wiggly stores, which opened in Memphis, TN, in 1916, are considered to be the first modern grocery stores.

HAIRDRESSER The first hair dryer may have been a vacuum cleaner! An early ad for a vacuum cleaner showed a woman using the exhaust to dry her hair.

Fascinating Facts

HORSE TRAINER Horses turn their ears toward the sounds they hear. They can even swivel their ears backwards to listen to sounds behind them.

HOUSE PAINTER Early house paints were mixed by hand in a messy, time-consuming process. Henry Sherwin wanted painting to be easier. In 1880, he made the first ready-mixed paint.

ICE SKATER Sonja Henie from Norway changed competitive ice skating by adding jumps and ballet moves to what were previously rather dull routines. By 1936, she had won ten world championships and three Olympic gold medals

JUDGE Thurgood Marshall became the first African-American Supreme Court justice in 1967. In 1981, Sandra Day O'Connor became the first woman on the Supreme Court.

LAWYER At various times and places in the United States, there have been laws against carrying an ice cream cone in your pocket, singing out of tune, hitching a crocodile to a fire hydrant, and sneezing on a train.

LIBRARIAN Colonel James Anderson made his library available to working boys in the 1850s. Andrew Carnegie never forgot this kindness, and by the time of his death in 1919, Carnegie had financed more than 2,500 libraries around the world.

LIFEGUARD Rufus Porter invented the first life preserver, which included shoes with a parachute-like device that opened up in the water.

MAIL CARRIER Mail carriers have not always traveled by truck or by foot. World-wide, mail carriers have used canoes, skis, camels, homing pigeons, and even stilts!

MARINE BIOLOGIST A baleen whale has no teeth. Instead, it has hundreds of stringy plates, called *baleen*, in its mouth. The whale uses the baleen to trap food.

MAYOR The first African-American mayor of a large city was Carl Stokes of Cleveland, elected in 1967. The first woman mayor, Susanna Medora Salter of Argonia, KS, did not know she had been nominated until she saw her name on the ballot.

MECHANIC The first Ford Model T sold for $825 in 1908. By 1927, 15 million Model Ts had been made.

METEOROLOGIST The hottest temperature on record was in Libya in 1922: 136.4° in the shade. The lowest temperature on record was in Antarctica in 1983: –128.6°.

MUSICIAN In 1995, pianist Helen Huang played with the New York Philharmonic Orchestra. She was only 12 years old at the time.

911 OPERATOR The first telephone call was an "emergency" call. When Alexander Graham Bell spilled acid on his pants, he used his new invention to call his assistant for help.

Fascinating Facts

NURSE Clara Barton was a nurse who helped wounded soldiers in the Civil War. She was an advocate for African Americans, helping an all-black regiment and later recruiting Frederick Douglass to serve on the board of the American Red Cross, which Barton created in 1881.

OPTOMETRIST Marco Polo reported seeing people wearing eyeglasses in China in the late 1200s. More than 400 years later, a British optician made the first eyeglass frames.

ORTHODONTIST The first braces were made by Pierre Fauchard in 1728. They consisted of a flat strip of metal fastened to the teeth by pieces of thread.

PALEONTOLOGIST There are 205,000 acres of dinosaur fossil beds in Dinosaur National Monument in Colorado and Utah.

PARAMEDIC Changes in highway safety laws in the 1960s led to training and certifying paramedics. Before that time, ambulance drivers often had no medical training.

PARENT The lullaby "Rock-a-Bye Baby" was written by 15-year-old Effie Crockett, a descendant of Davy Crockett.

PARK RANGER In 1872, President Ulysses S. Grant made Yellowstone the world's first national park. Today there are more than 50 national parks in the United States.

PET GROOMER A flea can jump 200 times the length of its own body and 100 times its height.

PHOTOGRAPHER George Eastman made the Kodak, the first camera designed for public use. The original camera took 100 pictures and had to be sent to the factory to be developed.

PILOT The first successful flight took place in 1903 at Kitty Hawk, NC. Orville Wright flew the plane he and his brother, Wilbur, had designed. The plane flew approximately 30 miles an hour for 12 seconds.

PLUMBER In the 1880s, only one out of six families had a bathtub.

POLICE OFFICER Fingerprinting became a reliable method of identifying criminals in the 1880s after a British anthropologist proved that no two people have the same fingerprint patterns.

PRESIDENT The president who served the longest term was Franklin D. Roosevelt: 12 years, 39 days. William Henry Harrison served the shortest term: 32 days.

PRINCIPAL In 1647, Massachusetts passed the first law to require public schools. For much of the year, students went to school from 7:00 A.M. until as late as 9:00 P.M., with a two-hour break in the afternoon.

REAL ESTATE AGENT Most American buildings are made of materials such as wood, bricks, and stone. The Corn Palace in Mitchell, SD, is made of ears of corn and grasses. It is often called the world's largest bird feeder.

Fascinating Facts

RECYCLING WORKER How about this for an unusual recycling idea? In 1922 Elis Stenman of Pigeon Cove, MA, filled an entire cottage with furniture made from newspaper—chairs, tables, a desk, a piano—even a grandfather clock!

REPORTER In 1885, Nellie Bly (whose real name was Elizabeth Cochrane) wrote a letter to the editor of the *Pittsburgh Dispatch* in response to an editorial against women working in men's jobs. The editor was so impressed, he offered her a job as a reporter.

RESEARCH SCIENTIST Marie Curie (1867–1934) was the first woman to win a Nobel Prize and the first person to win *two* Nobel Prizes.

SALES CLERK The Mall of America in Bloomington, MN, has more than 300 stores and even contains an amusement park!

SANITATION WORKER The average New Yorker produces approximately seven pounds of garbage a day. That's more than four million tons of garbage in New York City per year!

SCHOOL BUS DRIVER In 1869, the town of Quincy, MA, provided a wagon to take students to school. Soon, other school districts were using all kinds of vehicles for this purpose—even circus wagons, sleighs, and boats!

SPORTS OFFICIAL Sports officials need a lot of endurance. NBA referees run an estimated six miles per game. Hockey officials must be able to skate for 60 minutes.

TEACHER Mary McLeod Bethune was devoted to improving education for black children. She founded a school for girls in Daytona Beach, FL, that later became a college in 1923.

TENNIS PRO Tennis clothing has changed a lot since 1874, when the game was first played in the United States. At that time, men wore long pants, and women wore long skirts and long-sleeved shirts.

TRAIN CONDUCTOR The world's largest train station is Grand Central in New York City. An average of 550 trains and 200,000 commuters pass through the station daily.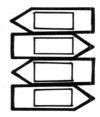

TRUCK DRIVER In contests that are called "roadeos," drivers of trucks, snow plows, or buses compete in special events for prizes.

 **VETERINARIAN** In the United States, the most popular breed of dog is the labrador retriever, while the most popular breed of cat is the Persian.

WAITER/WAITRESS In 1876, Fred Harvey opened a fine dining room in the Topeka railroad depot. It was a big hit, and Harvey made restaurant history when he hired women to serve the meals—the first waitresses.

ZOO KEEPER  The San Diego Zoo was one of the first American zoos to keep animals in more natural surroundings instead of cages.